Until the development of the railways, Cornish b rivers, not to cross valleys and so it was that until the were to be found spanning the widest rivers and est rivers, the Tamar and the Fowey, a number of smaller rivers – many of which feed into these two major rivers – and innumerable streams.

The Tamar – the 'Great Water' – almost makes Cornwall an island. It rises only four miles from the Atlantic coast north of Bude and flows, almost due south, down to Plymouth. Here, just below Saltash, it is joined by the River Lynher to form the Hamoaze estuary flowing into Plymouth Sound. For almost all its length it forms the border with Devon.

All three of the Tamar's main Cornish tributaries – the Ottery, the Kensey and the Inny – have their sources within a few miles of each other to the east of Boscastle. The most northerly, the Ottery, flows southeastwards to join the Tamar just upstream of Higher New Bridge, northeast of Launceston. The Kensey runs almost parallel to the Ottery, running through Launceston and joining the Tamar upstream of Polson Bridge. The Inny is the longest of the three, rising near Davidstow. At Two Bridges on the A30, it is joined by the Penpont Water, which drains the eastern side of Bodmin Moor and the river joins the Tamar between Greystone Bridge and Horsebridge.

The Lynher's source is also on the east of Bodmin Moor in Altarnun parish, flowing down to St Germans and onto Plymouth Sound. At St Germans, it is joined by the River Tiddy, whose source is to the northeast of Liskeard.

On the south coast, the only significant rivers between the Tiddy and Looe are the Seaton and the East Looe River. Further west, however, is the Fowey, the county's second most important river. It rises on Bodmin Moor, very close to the source of the Lynher, flows almost due south for 10 miles, then loops west before turning south again to run though Lostwithiel and onto the town of Fowey. On that westward loop, it is joined by three tributaries all running almost due south – the St Neot, the Warleggan (also known as the Bedalder) and Cardinham Water. These three all drain the south side of Bodmin Moor. South of Lostwithiel, the Fowey is joined by another, shorter, tributary river, the Lerryn.

West of Fowey, only minor rivers, such as the Luxulyan, which runs down to Par, and the St Austell River, are encountered until the Fal is reached. The Fal rises near Roche and loops north over Goss Moor before turning south westwards through Grampound and Tregony and onto Falmouth and into the world's third deepest estuary. The Allen, flowing southwards from its source near Zelah, and the Kenwyn flowing southwestwards, meet at Truro to form the Truro River, which in turn flows into the Fal. The latter's other major tributaries are the Tresillian, flowing westwards, and the little Kennal, flowing eastwards.

Allen is also the name for a tributary of the River Camel, to which it runs almost parallel from its source north of Camelford before turning and joining it just south of Wadebridge. The Camel itself has its source on Davidstow Moor, close to, but on the other side of the watershed from, the source of the Inny. It flows southwestwards before turning towards the sea at Padstow.

Davidstow Moor's importance in the county's water system was most clearly demonstrated on 8 July 1847. A waterspout suddenly burst on the moor, sending a wall of water 12 to 18 feet high surging along the Camel. Carrying with it whatever trees and rocks it could gather, it destroyed the Gam, Wenford, Poleys, Tresarret, Dunmeer bridges as well as the railway bridges at Dunmeer and Pendavy. Only

Helland and Wadebridge (surely not coincidentally the two oldest) were left standing. Bridges on the other side of the moor were not spared either. On the River Inny, all the bridges were swept away except the 16th century Trekelland Bridge.

The De Lank, which rises in Roughtor Marsh in the heart of Bodmin Moor, is another of the Camel's tributaries, meeting south of Poley's Bridge. Along its course are several simple but very picturesque bridges of interest.

Beyond the Camel, the only sizeable rivers are the Gannel (just to the south of Newquay) and the Hayle. Further west, on the Penwith peninsula, there are only minor streams until one turns east again and enters the Lizard Peninsula to find the Helford. But even this broad and lovely watercourse is fed by only minor streams.

It is on the Tamar and the Fowey, and at the head of estuaries such as the Camel that the county's largest bridges are to be found. However, viaducts (tall bridges crossing valleys) are to be seen throughout the county. And, although Cornwall has many large and impressive bridges, it also has hundreds of delightful small ones, a great many of which cross very minor waterways.

Polson Bridge over the Tamar DIANA CASHIN

The 17th century Polyphant Bridge

A HISTORY OF BRIDGES IN CORNWALL

Unsurprisingly, given the narrowness of the Cornish peninsula, the county has historically looked to the sea as a route for communication and trade rather than the land. Most early roads ran to the ports rather than towards the Tamar and the rest of England. A few roads also linked the north and south coasts – for example the Saint's Way incorporates part of a route from the Camel Estuary to the Fowey. Crantock on the Gannel – at one time a prosperous port – was linked to Truro by a road that ran almost due south through Cargoll and Idless.

There were some east-west routes however. These were ridgeway tracks – high roads avoiding boggy ground. Milestones found near Tintagel and at Marazion prove that they were in use at least in Roman times, if not earlier. Nevertheless, it was not until after the Norman Conquest, when Cornwall began to have an increasing involvement with the rest of England, that the main route into the county was over the Tamar at Polson Bridge. From here it went on to Launceston, over Polyphant Bridge to Bodmin and then onto the far west. This was the *via regalis Cornubiensis* – the King's Way of Cornwall, with a branch road to Camelford and Padstow. First mentioned in a charter of 1260, it has undergone innumerable improvements, not least the diversion away from Polyphant Bridge to Two Bridges in the early 19th century and the by-passing of Polson Bridge by Dunheved Bridge in the 1970s, but it remains to this day, under the label of the A30, the principal highway through the county.

A more southerly route crossed the River Tamar at Newbridge near Gunnislake,

The early 16th century New Bridge at Gunnislake

then on to Truro through Liskeard and Grampound, or to Looe on a branch road from Liskeard. An even more southerly route crossed the Hamoaze at Cremyll, ran onto Looe, and went on to Par, St Austell and Tregony and then on to St Michael's Mount and the far west.

This latter route crossed the Tamar, the Fowey and Fal not by bridges, but by ferries at Cremyll, the Bodinnick Passage and the King Harry Passage. Ferries were less expensive to maintain, and much less expensive to build, than bridges, and they played a key role in transportation for many centuries. Indeed, the King Harry Ferry (now a chain ferry, officially designated as a floating bridge) still operates, connecting the Roseland Peninsula with the Falmouth area. And it was not until 24 October 1961 that the ferry across the Tamar between Saltash and Plymouth was replaced by a bridge.

Where roads met rivers and streams and there was no ferry, perhaps because the water was too shallow, fording was the only option. Even in the nineteenth century three feet was an acceptable depth for a pedestrian; four feet for a horse and rider. The Cornish for ford is 'Ret' or 'Res', and there are many place names that reflect the location of a fording point, such as Respryn and Restronguet. The 'wade' in Wadebridge indicates that this too was the site of a ford long before the building of the bridge.

'Pons' and 'pon' in a placename, on the other hand, reflect the presence, or one-time presence, of a bridge. Examples are Ponsanooth ('new bridge'), Penpont ('bridgehead'), Chypons ('bridge house') and Pondhu ('black bridge'). That this is from the Latin *pons* and not from a Cornish word, strongly suggests that bridges may not have existed in the county in pre-Roman times.

There are claims that there are bridges in Polperro of Roman and Saxon origin, but they are much later. Even more disappointingly, although King Arthur may have fought his last battle at Slaughterbridge, there is no evidence of a bridge over the Camel there at that time, and, even worse, the name may derive not from the battle but from the word *slohtre* meaning a marsh or muddy place.

The earliest known reference to a bridge in Cornwall is to *Ponsprontiryon* ('priest's bridge') in the Penwith parish of Buryan, noted in 930 AD. The exact location is not known, but given the size of the watercourses in Buryan parish, this bridge would have been a small one. Crossing the Tamar was an altogether much more challenging proposition. The first bridge across is thought to be at Bridgerule (on a stretch of the upper river where both banks are in Devon), built in the early years after the Norman Conquest. However, shortly afterwards Launceston Castle was built by Robert of Mortain and this was soon followed by the construction of the Polson Bridge. It was to remain the principal point of entry into Cornwall for centuries. Rebuilt in 1852, it was eventually superceded by the Dunheved Bridge in 1976.

Less enduring has been the route between Launceston and Rillaton, once another major highway, but now an unclassified road leading to a tiny hamlet. The bridge on the road across the River Lynher was recorded in 1170 as *Pons lapideus* – 'stone bridge'. Such a bridge was merited by the important administrative centre that Rillaton then was. The bridge itself was rebuilt in the 1890s, but the nearby Starabridge may give an impression of its earlier appearance.

Although the Norman Conquest has had an unremittingly bad press over the last 940 years, it did produce stability and, as a direct consequence, a steady growth in trade. In the following centuries, more and more bridges were built probably to cope with the increasing packhorse traffic. Bridges at St Erth, Druxton and Helland

Starabridge: a medieval survivor

Yeolm Bridge – the oldest dated bridge in Cornwall

were all erected in the 14th century, as were those at Yeolm – the oldest surviving bridge in the county – and Respryn, a major strategic point on the Bodmin to Looe road.

Truro's first bridges – the East Bridge (on Old Bridge Street) and West Bridge (over the Kenwyn River, where Victoria Square is today) were probably both built in the early 14th century and – although presumably much repaired – the latter was described four hundred years later as just wide enough for packhorses, with a ford and stepping stones alongside.

Nevertheless, if there was a Golden Age of Cornish bridge building, it was undoubtedly the 15th century. This saw the erection of Horsebridge and Greystone (very probably by the same builder), Treverbyn, Panter's, Ruthern, the New Bridge over the Lynher, Higher New Bridge at Launceston, Plusha, and Clapper. It was also in this century that the longest bridges were constructed the seventeen-arch bridge at Wadebridge and the 15-arch bridge at Looe. Whereas the former has been widened many times over the centuries, sadly the old bridge at Looe, said to be only 6ft 2in. in width, was pulled down in and replaced with the current bridge, some 100 yards downstream, in 1853.

As noted earlier, Wadebridge owes part

The 15th century Horsebridge

The stone Clapper Bridge over the Lynher

of its name to a ford, but the bridge was a replacement for a ferry, as recorded by John Leland in 1535.

'Wher as now Wadebridge is there was a Fery 80 Yeres syns, and Menne sumtyme passing over by Horse stood oftern in great Jeopardie. Then one Lovebone, Vicar of Wadebridge, movid with pitie began the bridge, and with great Paine and Studre, good people putting their Help, thereto, finished it with xvi fair and great uniform Arches of Stone. One told me that the Fundation of certein of the arches was first sette on so quik sandy Ground that Lovebone almost despairid to performe the Bridg ontyl such tyme as he layed Pakkes of Wolle for Fundation.'

The county's best known packhorse bridge also dates from the 15th century. Packhorses were the predominant mode of transport in Cornwall's steep valleys, and still the main means of transporting mineral ores up until the early 19th century. Crossing the River Kensey at Newport, Launceston, the packhorse bridge is both scheduled as an Ancient Monument and Listed Grade I. It is sometimes referred to as St Thomas's Bridge – the name also given to the 18th century road bridge some 85m downstream. Launceston Priory was relocated beside the church of St Thomas in 1155 from its former site at St Stephens to the north and until the building of the bridge the nearby ford upstream would have been the only means of crossing to the settlement of Newport to the north.

The bridge, its iron stanchions and its 19th century gas lamp (now converted to electricity), create a picturesque setting, but what appears to be a simpler packhorse bridge survives at Porthcothan Mill. The earliest records of the mill are from the 1590s, but the style of the bridge suggests that it could be earlier.

The New Bridge at Gunnislake, New Bridge over the Fowey, and those at Lerryn, St Austell and Berriow all date from the 16th century – the last great bridges of the county until the coming of the railways. This was the result, not of a sufficiency of bridges, but a lack of money. Although the maintenance of large bridges could be funded by tolls, financing their construction was a major burden on the local economy. Few would have been built had it not been for assistance – direct and indirect – of the Church. Bridge-building was regarded as a pious work and the necessary finance for construction was raised by the selling of Indulgences (remission from time spent in Purgatory, usually 40 days) and

The Grade I packhorse bridge at Launceston

obit bequests (masses sung on the anniversary of one's death). More directly, the Church had its own bridge designers – a French Order of Bridge Building Friars. One member of this may even have worked in Cornwall: Thomas de Ponte was given a

The 16th century Lerryn Bridge

The tiny Polwheveral Bridge

Charter of Protection and Letters of Indulgence by the Bishop of Exeter in 1259 for building and repairing bridges in the Diocese.

The Church connection was sometimes incorporated in the architecture: the Looe bridge of 1418 had a chapel in the centre and Lostwithiel Bridge had a chapel at one end. In at least one instance, religion was the entire reason for a bridge's construction: Plusha Bridge is said to have been built so that the miners of Caradon could easily reach their parish church at Linkinhorne.

With the Reformation (which was partly fuelled by the corruption associated with the selling of Indulgences) the first great era of bridge building was over. And not only did bridges lose their religious character but financing repairs became more and more of a problem, one that could not be solved by tolls alone. Responsibility passed to the Justices of the Quarter Sessions, who had the power to enforce a rate for repairs on the parish or the county. Not surprisingly, this proved both time-consuming and unpopular. Of the large bridges, it seems that only the bridge at Wadebridge, which had an endowment of land, was capable of financing itself.

There were, of course, a great many other smaller bridges being constructed throughout the county and throughout the centuries. Written records relating to them are extremely rare, but one exception is the Polwheveral Bridge, an easily-missed structure on a minor road just south of Constantine, near Falmouth, the contract for which has survived:

May 24th, 1572. Memo: that one Roger Hallard of Tregony Borough, Mason, hath bargained to make of new-hewed stone of moore stone one Bridge now decayed in Polwheverell before the day of St. James the Apostle next ensueing under the manner and form following:

First, the same Bridge is to be made with an Arch of hewn stone, the water course between the two side walls to be 7 foot broad with 2 squinches on the upper side and

The 17th century Keybridge over the De Lank

the walls of every end of the side walls to be of length 12 foot, and to make two crests of every side of the passage and ye Bridge to be hewn stone above the Bridge rising 2 foot; and between the same 2 crests to be clear 7 foot way for wain carriage and the Bridge and the Arch to rise in altitude 7 foot and the parish to pay him for his labour £3 6s. 8d. and to find cleavers and all lime and sand. And the said Roger to be bound in £6 13s. 4d. to the parish to perform this bargaine and alsoe to maintain and repair the same Bridge at his cost and charges during his life; whereof paid him present in part of payment 6s. 8d.

Item, he must enclose the way on the back of the Bridge with hewed stone to be well pinned and he to cleave and occupy in the same works such rocks and stones as now lye in the way in Polwheverell Lane annoying the passage.

And of the payments the rest to be 20s. more after one week's work begun, 20s. more in the middle of the work and the rest in the end thereof.

Thus the maintenance problem was ingeniously solved by making the builder responsible for the rest of his day. Although widened in the 19th century, the bridge remains much as Roger Hallard built it.

After the flurry of 15th and 16th centuries, the 17th century saw relatively little bridge building activity. Nevertheless, some interesting structures were built around Bodmin Moor at Polyphant, Keybridge, Altarnun and Bradford. However, there was considerable activity of another kind on other bridges in the county – as battlefields of the Civil War. In July 1644 Lord Essex took New Bridge at Gunnislake from Sir Richard Grenville, with the loss of 40 of his men and some 200 on the Royalist side. A month later the King crossed into Cornwall and defeated Essex at Lostwithiel, then returned up country over the New Bridge. Two years later, at the end of February 1646, General Fairfax took Tamerton Bridge after a fierce struggle. Shortly after, on 10 March 1646, a conference was held at Tresillian Bridge between Fairfax, whose

Altarnun Bridge, restored back to its original appearance

army was now at Tregony and Lord Hopton, whose Royalist army was stationed in Truro. This was the beginning of the treaty, signed two days later at Truro, that ended the first Civil War.

The ornamental bridge in the grounds of Chyverton House is one of a small number of interesting surviving 18th century bridges. Nanny Moore's Bridge near the seafront at Bude, which has a cantilevered section which can be raised to allow boats on the River Neet to pass, is thought to be 18th century, although, as it leads to the site of a 16th century tidemill, it may be older. The name is however much later: Nanny Moore was a 19th century beach attendant who lived nearby. Trewornan Bridge, which crosses the River Amble, a tributary of the Camel on the other hand, has the appearance of a medieval structure, with its four pointed arches, but was in fact built in 1791, under the direction of the local vicar, William Sandys.

Nanny Moore's Bridge at Bude

The 'Gothic' Treworan Bridge

13

A semi-circular refuge on Marazion Old Bridge

Finally, Marazion Old Bridge, north west of the town, just off the seafront road and lying within sight of St Michael's Mount, is a rare example of a completely unaltered 18th century bridge. It owes its survival to the building, just a few yards away, of the wider Marazion Bridge in 1837. And this latter bridge was part of what might be called Cornwall's second Golden Age of Bridge Building – the era of the turnpikes.

Throughout Britain, maintenance of roads had for centuries been as intractable a problem as the maintenance of bridges. As early as 1555, Mary Tudor had passed legislation to force parishes to take responsibility for road repair, but this did not result in action. It was not until the beginning of the 18th century that a new and effective solution emerged – the turnpike trusts. These trusts took over responsibility for the building and repair of roads, in return for levying tolls. By the 1840s over 20,000 miles in Britain were run by turnpike trusts.

Truro was the first Cornish town to establish a trust, in 1754, to bring roads into the town. Launceston, Callington and Bodmin followed in the 1760s and this decade also saw the longer distance routes established. 1825 and 1839 saw more flurries of activity and in 1863, at the very end of the turnpike era, a trust took over responsibility for the Penzance–St Just road.

A reminder of this system is Marazion's Turnpike Road, which would once have linked the town with Falmouth but the regular occurrence of milestones is usually itself is an indication of an old turnpike.

Where a turnpike crossed water, it was the responsibility of the trust to either repair existing or build new bridges. The bridge at Perranarworthal on the Truro to Falmouth road – a turnpike of 1823 – is one example.

Another turnpike road bridge lies on the narrow unclassified road that leads from the A30 to the village of Temple. It is perhaps a little unspectacular as a bridge, but a good illustration of the work of the turnpike trusts. The village derives its name from the Knights Templar who founded a hospice on Bodmin Moor in the 12th century. The knights also built causeways over the marshy ground that forms the headwaters of the River Warleggan. These causeways defined part of the main road from Launceston to Bodmin for centuries and when the Turnpike Act for the improvement of the road was passed in 1769, the causeways were refurbished. However, instead of continuing to use the medieval paved ford that lay on the road, a new small bridge was built. But the twisting route through the village proved troublesome and within less than a century, the road was diverted and a new bridge built. This has itself been refurbished and enlarged to form part of the A30, leaving

Temple Old Bridge as a rare and largely unaltered example of a bridge built specifically for a turnpike.

Although 'turnpike fever' gripped the whole nation, not every bridge built at this time was financed by the turnpike trusts. King William's Bridge in Morwenstow was built in 1836, and as its inscription states, it was paid for by public subscription, twenty pounds coming from William IV himself.

By the time Temple New Bridge was being built, the age of the turnpike was coming to an end and in the 1870s the trusts were wound up throughout the country and their duties passed to the Highways Boards, the precursors of the county councils. The demise of the turnpike trusts was precipitated by a decline in tolls, thanks to the new transport technologies   the canals and the railways.

The potential for canals in Cornwall, with its hilly terrain, was limited, and although several were proposed, few were built. An exception was the Bude Canal. This had been proposed in 1774 by John Edyvean, who the previous year had suggested a canal from Mawgan Porth through parishes inland and back to St Columb Porth and even succeeding in getting two sections dug. However, the idea of the Bude Canal had to wait until 1818 to be revived by James Green, Surveyor of Bridges and Buildings in Devon, and the Holsworthy surveyor, Thomas Shearn. Work began in 1819 and the canal, with branches to Holsworthy and the Tamar at Druxton Bridge, was completed in 1825. Its principal purpose was to take Bude sea sand – rich in nutrients – to farms in the surrounding area, but it also carried considerable quantities of coal. There were only three locks on the canal: height was achieved by inclined planes, up which the small wheeled barges – 'tub boats' – were dragged along rails.

Old Temple Bridge on the old turnpike road

The Bude Canal bridge at Helebridge

Helebridge marked the limit for conventional barges – beyond this only tub boats could navigate. And here James Green built a particularly elegant bridge over the canal. Other bridge relics of the canal, which was abandoned in 1891, are to be found near Burmsdon Farmhouse at Launcells and the Haunch Bridge at Boyton. The inclined plane in Werrington has an integral bridge.

Another integral bridge in an inclined plane can be seen at Portreath, but the incline was for a different mode of transport. It was the final length of the Hayle Railway's Portreath branch of 1837 that brought copper from the mines around Carn Brea to the harbour.

The industrial revolution's demand for Cornwall's minerals led to the development of many railway lines in the early years of the nineteenth century, and the landscape of Cornwall is rich in their relics, which include bridges. At Rough Street just outside Lanner, for example, a

The Portreath incline

bridge carries the route of a line built in 1838 to serve the Tresavean Mine half a mile away, at that time the county's third largest producer of copper.

But undoubtedly the most spectacular relic of mineral transportation was the result of an entrepreneur combining both canal and rail transport. Joseph Thomas (Austen) Treffry of Fowey, owner of one of the greatest copper mines in the area (Fowey Consols) constructed a canal from Par to Ponts Mill. This linked to a horse-drawn tramway that ran to Bugle, climbed the Luxulyan valley on an inclined plane, powered by a waterwheel, and crossed it by a viaduct to link up with his nearby granite quarries.

The granite voussoirs on Treffry's Viaduct

The most spectacular structure in this early integrated transport system was, of course, the viaduct across the Luxulyan Valley. Known as Treffry's Viaduct, it was built between 1839 and 1842 (under the supervision of Treffry's land steward, William Pease). The first all-stone viaduct in the county, it was built entirely of granite from Treffry's own quarries. Even the sleepers on which the rails were mounted were granite. It was however not only a viaduct: it was also an aqueduct, carrying water in channels below the sleepers to a complicated leat system to power machinery in the valley and in the mines.

The viaduct stands 90 feet above the valley floor and its 10 arches give it an overall length of nearly 600 feet. On the northern side is the Treffry Coat of Arms, with its motto *'Dum Deo Placuerit'* – 'While God will'.

Treffry was also responsible for the Tolcarne Viaduct, known as the Tolcarne Spider. This seventeen-pillared structure was topped with wooden trestles 58 feet above the Trenance valley floor and carried the horse-drawn tramway from Hendra Clay Pit to Newquay. The Cornwall Minerals Railway took over the line in 1874, replacing the trestles with iron girders. However, some of the masonry from the original structure can still be seen.

The numerous mineral lines undoubtedly carried passengers in their trucks now and then, but the county's first true passenger service began in 1834 on the Bodmin & Wadebridge Railway. The Hayle Railway – running between Hayle and Redruth – opened four years later but did not start a passenger service until 1843. The terrain here was much hillier than at Wadebridge, and the locomotives were helped up the steep inclines at Penponds and Angarrack by the use of cables. In 1846 the Hayle Railway was taken over by a new company, the West Cornwall Railway, who set out to extend the line into a route between Truro and Penzance. The engineer appointed for the task was Isambard Kingdom Brunel, the greatest of the Victorian engineers. For the 26-mile West Cornwall line, which opened in 1852, Brunel designed nine viaducts, including ones at Penponds and Angarrack to avoid the inclines. If all nine were laid end-to-end, they would extend over a mile.

At the same time as he was appointed Engineer for the West Cornwall Railway, Brunel also accepted the post of Engineer for the Cornwall Railway (whose chairman at this time was none other than Joseph Treffry). This company proposed to build a

The viaduct at Angarrack, built 1885

line linking Falmouth with the Plymouth terminus of the South Devon Railway (Engineer: I.K. Brunel), which linked, via the Bristol & Exeter Railway (Engineer: I.K. Brunel), with the Bristol-London Great Western Railway (Engineer: I.K. Brunel). For the railway to reach Truro from Plymouth, a distance of fifty-three miles, thirty-four viaducts were built – which, again, if laid end-to-end, would stretch for more than four miles.

The Cornwall Railway line was opened in 1859, the year of Brunel's death, so he did not live to see the final leg of the line from Truro to Falmouth, which opened four years later. Constructed by his chief assistant, Robert Brereton, it needed another mile of viaducts, eight in number.

To save money, both the West Cornwall Railway and the Cornwall Railway lines were single track (although on the Cornwall Railway, the single track was Brunel's broad gauge of 7ft ¹/₄ in.). And wood was used extensively in their construction. Some, such as those on the West Cornwall Railway, were entirely wooden; others had masonry piers from which a fan-like arrangement of timbers spread to carry the wooden deck. The longest was at Truro (1,329ft) and the highest at St. Pinnock (151ft above the valley).

Brunel had warned from the outset that the construction was a false economy and that maintenance of the wooden structures would be high after the first ten years and it would be an ongoing commitment. From 1881, they started to be replaced, mostly with masonry arches, but some with iron girders and some with embankments. But the replacement programme itself was undertaken in several

The original Collegewood viaduct at Penryn in 1915

Moorswater Viaduct, with Brunel's old piers still standing

phases and took sixty-three years. It was not until 1934 that the very last timber viaduct in Cornwall, at Collegewood on the Falmouth branch, was dismantled.

Some of the replacements re-used the original piers, widened to take a double line of the standard gauge track, but others were built on new alignments, and the old masonry piers were left standing.

The new piers are simple and functional. The old piers, particularly those at Moorswater with their buttresses and gothic-style openings, have a cathedral-like quality. This care and attention to detail to create something that does not merely do its job but also looks pleasing can be seen not only on the old viaduct piers but in the most modest of bridges. At Wainsford, between the Derrycombe and Penadlake viaducts, an accommodation bridge was built through the embankment, to link two farm fields. This cartway is only seven feet wide, but nevertheless nothing has been scrimped to produce a finely finished vaulted ceiling and sturdy abutments.

The accommodation bridge at Wainsford is a small, intact reminder of Brunel's

***The accommodation bridge through
the railway embankment at
Wainsford***

contribution to the Cornish landscape. There is however a much more colossal reminder of the great engineer's contribution – the railway bridge over the River Tamar at Saltash.

Of all Brunel's bridges throughout the country, the Royal Albert Bridge at Saltash is his masterpiece. In engineering history, it is one of the world's most important bridges. Even by the remarkable standards of Victorian engineering it was a truly outstanding achievement.

The Cornwall Railway originally planned to cross the Tamar lower down on the Hamoaze by a 'steam bridge' (a ferry), a scheme initially supported by Brunel. However, once he had conducted his own survey, he decided the better solution was a bridge at Saltash where the river narrowed to 1,100ft and had steep banks on both sides. The latter was

The Royal Albert Bridge, Saltash

Saltash Bridge

crucial because the bridge had to be at a high level – not for engineering reasons but because the Tamar is a navigable river. As such, it was not the Engineer but the Lord High Admiral who determined the height of the bridge. It was to be 100ft between high water and the soffit (the underside of the deck) of the bridge.

Brunel's eventual design was for a two-span bridge with a central pier. The building of this pier was a significant achievement in its own right: never before had a foundation been built at such a depth. To achieve it, a 300-ton wrought iron cylinder, 37ft in diameter and 90ft tall was constructed and sunk to the riverbed, $87^1/_2$ ft below high water. This acted as a cofferdam for up to 40 men to build the masonry foundation. It took $2^1/_2$ years.

Once the masonry was built up to the water level, the western iron span was floated out on pontoons and manoeuvred into position. It was jacked up inch by inch, with the masonry bricks being laid under it as it rose. Once completed, the process was repeated with the eastern span. The bridge was finally opened by Prince Albert on 2 May 1959.

Missing from the ceremony were the dignitaries from Truro (due to a locomotive failure) and Brunel himself. Diagnosed with Bright's Disease and suffering from stress induced by the building and launch of the steamship *Great Eastern*, he had been ordered by his doctor to recuperate in Egypt and he did not return to England in time for the opening of the bridge. Nevertheless, later that month, a train crossed the bridge with just one passenger: the great engineer himself. A few months later, he was dead. Shortly afterwards, the directors of the Cornwall Railway agreed to erect the letters 'I K BRUNEL ENGINEER 1859' at both ends of the bridge's portals as a memorial. Now, a century and a half later, although strengthened to carry the heavier trains of today, the bridge still carries the main line into the county.

It was not until nearly half a century after the opening of the Royal Albert Bridge that the tidal Tamar was crossed again by a railway bridge. In 1891 the Plymouth, Devonport & South Western Junction Railway took over the old East Cornwall Mineral Railway, which served the mines around Gunnislake, Stoke Climsland and Kelly Bray (a mile to the north of Callington) and the quarries of Kit Hill. The new owners converted it from a $3^1/_2$ ft line to standard gauge and built a new line to connect with their own track at Bere Alston in Devon. To cross the Tamar, a twelve-arch single-track viaduct was built at Calstock, and opened in 1908.

It was intended that most of the mineral freight would travel through Calstock to Bere Alston, but it was recognised that Calstock Quay, 120 feet below the viaduct, might still play an important role. An ingenious lift was built, operated by a steam winding engine, which was capable of lowering a 20 ton wagon from the viaduct to the quay. Over the years, however, it became used less and less frequently and in 1934 it was dismantled. The viaduct, on the other hand, is still in regular use, as part of the Plymouth-Gunnislake passenger line.

The Viaduct at Calstock, opened in 1908

Another half century passed and yet another bridge was built across the

Tamar. This, however, was a road bridge, jointly owned by Plymouth City Council and Cornwall County Council. Work began on the Tamar Bridge, just upstream from the Royal Albert Bridge, in July 1959 and it was open for traffic in October 1961. It was officially opened on 26 April 1962 by Queen Elizabeth the Queen Mother. With a main span of 1,100ft and the two side spans each of 374ft, it was at that time the largest bridge in the UK. It also the first toll bridge in the county for a century, although tolls are only levied on those leaving Cornwall. Traffic was carried on three lanes, with cyclists and pedestrians using the wide walkways.

By the mid-1990s the Tamar Bridge was carrying 40,000 vehicles a day, and with the ever-increasing weights of lorries, it was clearly not going to cope with 21st century traffic. Like all the county's major road bridges in all the preceding centuries, it was widened. Uniquely, however, it was widened without having to close. Work started in 1998 to hang a new carriageway on either side and strengthen the structure of the bridge and was completed by 20 December 2001. One of the new carriageways is dedicated to cyclists and pedestrians and, as it is on the downstream side, it gives an unrivalled view of the Royal Albert Bridge.

There has been another bridge built over the Tamar, but unlike the Tamar Bridge, which is unmissable, only a name sign and a warning of winds announces its presence. The Dunheved Bridge crosses near Launceston, making the old Polson Bridge redundant. Hundreds of thousands of cars use this bridge every year, but probably very few have any idea that they are even on a bridge, so invisibly does it merge with the roadway.

The asymmetrical Black Bridge at Hayle

The Iron Bridge at the Perran Iron Works, Perranarworthal

MATERIALS FOR BRIDGES

Until only very recently, bridges have invariably been made entirely of locally available materials. Undoubtedly many bridges were at one time wooden, either in total or in part. As we have seen, wood was still being used in the mid-nineteenth century as the principal building material for the viaducts on the Plymouth to Penzance line. However, today the only wooden bridges in the county are ornamental ones of recent origin, such as the Trellissick Garden bridge crossing the B3289. Stone – a material in which Cornwall is especially rich – is an enduring material, and the overwhelming majority of the county's bridges are of local stone.

Most of Cornwall consists of Devonian rocks, which are sedimentary rocks formed 400-440 million years ago which have been metamorphised into slate-like rock by the pressure of the subsequent ages. The local name for such stone is 'killas'.

The county also has considerable quantities of granite, with substantial amounts on Bodmin Moor, the Helman Tor area, Carnmenellis and on the Land's End peninsula beyond Penzance and St Ives. Almost all the stone bridges in the county are of killas, of granite or of both. Granite is common for piers and the coping on parapets, with the parapets themselves of killas rubble.

Brick is not a common material for building entire bridges in Cornwall – only a few railway bridges use this material exclusively. However, brick is sometimes used decoratively. A fine example is the carriageway bridge at Chyverton House, which has brick arch rings within a stone block structure.

Black Bridge, also called Sea Lane Bridge, in Hayle is formed from another kind of brick – scoria blocks, which are formed from the slag resulting after copper smelting. This early 19th century bridge is a reminder of a local enterprise – unfortunately short lived – to break the South Wales monopoly in smelting.

Cornwall also has an iron bridge of an early date, although at least 20 years younger than the famous Iron Bridge at Coalbrookdale. It is situated in the Perran Iron Foundry at Perranarworthal, and is a simple beam footbridge with two gothic style balustraded parapets, each cast as a single piece. The foundry was established in 1791 and was once the most important in Cornwall, responsible for producing some of the largest beam engines ever made.

Today concrete is ubiquitous as a bridge building material, but possibly the first example in Cornwall of its use for bridges is the five-arch viaduct at Poundstock, built in 1898 of 'rusticated' concrete blocks. A later but even more impressive example of same idea is the twelve-span viaduct at Calstock completed in 1908 . Even though granite was plentiful in the area, 11,148 concrete blocks were cast on site to build this 850ft long viaduct 120ft above the river.

The late 20th century saw bridge builders employ a wide range of new materials, and one of the most interesting in Britain is the Halgavor Bridge, which crosses the A30 just south of Bodmin. Part of the UK National Cycle Network and carrying pedestrians, horses and bikes across the route, it was designed by the architects Wilkinson Eyre who produced the award winning 'winking eye' bridge in Gateshead. It is a suspension bridge with a deck of GRP – or to be absolutely precise, glass-reinforced vinyl ester resin composite-topped with a surface made from re-cycled car tyres. Its great advantage is the minimal maintenance required.

The Halgavor suspension bridge

A simple plank beam bridge over a stream at Angarrack

TYPES OF BRIDGES

With the exception of some recent highway bridges, no two bridges are ever quite identical, even when they are very closely sited and crossing the same width of water. Nevertheless, bridges fall into a very small number of categories. There are, broadly, five types – beam, arch, cantilever, suspension and cable-stayed. Each 'works' in a slightly different way. There are examples of all five in Cornwall.

Beam bridges are the simplest of bridges. Occasionally on woodland walks one finds the very simplest of them all – a tree trunk over a small stream. It is believed that all bridges are a development from such a 'natural bridge'. A wooden plank is an obvious material to substitute for the trunk, but stone is even better as it can bear much greater loads. There are literally hundreds of stone beam bridges in the county, made of long lintel-like slabs of granite. Stone beam bridges are often called 'clapper' bridges. A simple, pretty but purely decorative example can be seen in the garden at the Barbara Hepworth Museum, St Ives, but exactly the same principle is used to create bridges capable of carrying heavy traffic.

A simple stone beam bridge in Barbara Hepworth's garden, St Ives

The unsurfaced beam bridge on Penberth beach

There are however severe limitations to the stone beam bridge. To be manoeuvrable, the stone beams can be neither very wide nor very long. However this obstacle can be overcome by laying a number of beams side-by-side, to increase the width, and by laying the beams end-to-end, supported by piers in the water (in effect building a number of beam bridges in a line) to increase the length of the bridge.

The tops of almost all stone beam bridges used by traffic are now covered with tarmac, making the construction visible only from underneath. However, in Penberth, by the foreshore there is a rare unsurfaced bridge over a stream. This has two sets of five beams laid side-by-side. There is another unsurfaced bridge near Roughtor Farm on Bodmin Moor.

Gam Bridge on the River Camel is probably the county's largest stone beam bridge and it illustrates both the possibilities and limitations of the beam bridge. It crosses the river at a point where it is about 45 ft wide. This required six piers to be erected in the water. Although the builders have managed to give the bridge a little 'hump' (usually beam bridges are quite flat), it is obvious that no boat of a practical size could pass between the piers or under the spans. Beam bridges usually make waterways unnavigable.

In simple terms, on all beam bridges, whether wood, stone or iron, the top of the beam is in compression (which causes it to shorten) and the bottom is in tension (which causes it to lengthen). It is usually imperceptible except perhaps on a long plank bridge, but every beam bridge sags in the middle under its own weight (known as the dead load), even a stone one. If the additional weight put on by people walking over it is too great, it will sag further and break, as it will if the supports at its ends are too far apart. There are, however, ways of strengthening the beam. One is internal – modern highway bridges often employ a beam of concrete reinforced with pre-stressed steel rods.

Gam Bridge over the Camel

The old railway bridge alongside the Camel estuary

The other method is external and is found on iron beam bridges. A lattice-like structure – a truss – can be fixed to the beam to give extra rigidity. When traffic moves over such a bridge, the compression is spread through the truss. This is particularly common on railway bridges. On these the 'beam' is usually two girders between which a deck is laid, and a truss is attached to both. A large example is the old railway bridge which once carried the Padstow–Wadebridge line over the Camel Estuary and now carries the Camel Trail. This three span bridge has tall trusses on all spans.

The biggest truss in the county is however on Saltash's Royal Albert Bridge. However, unlike most of the other trussed bridges in the world, the ends of the truss are not attached directly to the deck but are closed by towers of the bridge. This is because the Royal Albert Bridge is not simply a beam bridge with a truss: it combines this with another type of bridge – the suspension bridge, which will be discussed shortly.

Other trusses on iron bridges are more modest in scale. For example, the footbridge at Redruth station has a truss supporting the wooden deck. It was built when the line was being broadened into dual track and its date of build and its ownership (the line was then in the hands of the Great Western Railway) are commemorated in the decoration. The supporting piers at each end consist of four cast iron columns, the capitals of which are decorated in the 'Egyptian' style of the Victorian age.

Egyptian influence at Redruth

One iron beam bridge – the footbridge at Perran Iron Works – is a Scheduled Ancient Monument. Nearly all the other Scheduled bridges in Cornwall are of the second type – the **arch bridge**. The most obvious advantage that the arch has over the square opening of the beam bridge is that, for the same width, there is a greater height, which can mean that boats can more easily sail through. But, because an arch is made up of several components rather than a single member, the bridge span can be much wider too, which means fewer piers. Finally, the arch is also stronger than a stone beam bridge. All the parts are kept in compression (tension is negligible) and weight is transferred downwards *and* outwards. However, the ends of the arch have a natural tendancy to spring apart, so it has to be restrained by very substantial masonry on the river or valley banks.

Arches come in four main styles: semi-circular, pointed (or gothic), segmental and elliptical. The earliest form is the semi-circular, which was perfected in Roman times. It involved barrel vaulting, using wedge shaped blocks (voussoirs). When being built, such arches needed considerable shoring up until the mortar was set. Towards the end of the 12th century AD, the pointed arch began to be seen in ecclesiastical buildings and was seized upon by bridge builders, probably for both its practical values and its aesthetic qualities. On a multi-span bridge with pointed arches, the spans could be all the same height without being the same width (which would be impossible with a semi-circular arch) and even if it sagged a little as it settled, the appearance would not be spoilt. And it gave even more headroom for boats passing underneath.

The pointed arch does however have one significant disadvantage: its span is not as wide for its height as the span of a semi-circular arch. Therefore more spans are needed on a pointed arch bridge. It was nevertheless popular because it was used in conjunction with a new building technique, again taken from ecclesiastical construction – rib vaulting. Instead of creating an entire brick vault, a number of ribs were built and the spaces between them filled with stones that did not need to be cut as accurately as voussoirs.

After 1,600 years of building semi-circular arches, it was discovered in the 14th century that an arch that used just a segment of a circle was just as effective as a semi-circle. A segmental arch bridge, because it is flatter than both the semi-circular and the pointed arch, has less of a 'hump' (which is good for carts) and, as the segments are wider than the arched of a pointed arch bridge, it requires fewer piers. However, it could only be used where the banks were relatively high, or on rivers

that were not navigable by boats of any size, as the arch is much lower than on the other two types.

From this was developed the elliptical arch – formed from a segment of an ellipse, rather than of a circle. Although the legendary 12th century Pont d'Avignon has elliptical arches, it was not until Jean-Rodolfe Perronet built the Parisian bridges in the 18th century that the form was rediscovered. The elliptical arch is even flatter than the segmental arch, but its real value was aesthetic – the elliptical arch is a very beautiful shape.

Unfortunately, the shape of an arch is of little help in dating a bridge. It indicates only what its earliest

Rib construction on Yeolm Bridge

A pretty village bridge at St Neots

date can be, not its latest date. None of these arches replaced a previous form; they merely became part of the bridge builder's palette. Furthermore, it is often very difficult to tell what shape an arch is. A little subsidence over the years can make a pointed arch look semi-circular, and vice versa.

Cornwall's earliest datable surviving bridge is in fact a pointed-arch bridge. Built around 1300, the two-arch Yeolm Bridge over the Ottery is also a splendid example of rib construction and is remarkably similar to the north gate on Launceston Castle. Other examples of pointed arches are Treverbyn, Helland, Panter's Bridge, St Neot, Lerryn, Trekelland and the five-arch Lostwithiel bridge. The largest is the bridge at Wadebridge, which still has 15 out of its original 17 arches open, but unfortunately successive widenings have largely concealed the pointed arches.

New Bridge at Gunnislake, probably built in the early 16th century, has six pointed arches, but each is so broad that they almost appear semi-circular. Keybridge which crosses the De Lank, another 16th century bridge, is even more confusing: it has two arches, one is pointed and the other round.

Apart from the late 18th century Trewornan Bridge, which, as noted, was built in a medieval style, the pointed arch was not a feature of new bridges in the county after the 16th century. There are many beautiful semi-circular arch bridges before and after this date. Perhaps the two finest examples are Greystone and Horsebridge, both over the Tamar.

Semi-circular arches at Gweek

29

Clapper Bridge, which once must surely have been a stone beam bridge, is now a semi-circular arch bridge over the Lynher, built in the late 17th or early 18th century. There are many smaller but equally lovely semi-circular arch bridges, for example at Polyphant Bridge and Gweek.

Semi-circular arch bridges are also, literally, the greatest bridges of Cornwall – the railway viaducts. The Treffry Viaduct, the Calstock Viaduct and the majority of the replacements from Brunel's wooden structures all use the semi-circular form, supported on extremely tall piers.

The much-widened Wadebridge

Just as semi-circular arches can be difficult to distinguish from pointed arches, the difference between a semi-circular and segmental arch is not always entirely obvious. However, the county's true segmental arch bridges all date from between the end of the 18th and the middle of the 19th centuries. They range from the single span at Tregony to the bridge at Wadebridge. On the latter, segmental arches were built outside the original pointed arches in 1847 to widen the bridge by six feet. In 1963, the bridge was widened yet again on the upstream side, to practically double its width, again using segmental arches.

The Black Bridge at Hayle is also a segmental arch bridge, as well as a striking example of the use of local materials. But whereas on most arch bridges, of whatever shape, there is an attempt to keep the spans roughly the same height, this is not the case here. The two segmental arches differ in both height and span.

Elliptical arches are much rarer – perhaps because they are a little more difficult to build than segmental arches and have no structural advantage. Nevertheless, there are a few examples scattered around the county, such as the Old Bridge in Truro, Ham Mills Bridge, Nankelly Bridge and Haunch Bridge.

Whereas the segmental and elliptical arch offered flatter and therefore lower arches than the semi-circular arch, the accommodation bridge through a railway embankment sets a different challenge. Here, instead of a low long arch being desirable, a high and narrow arch is preferable. The accommodation bridge at Wainsford provides this by springing a segmental arch from the abutments at a height of over six feet. An even more elegant solution (where height was even less of a problem) is to be found just outside Penryn where the Truro-Falmouth line passes over the Hillhead Road, and is a particularly fine example of a parabolic arch.

A feature of bridges with more than one arch, and multi-span beam bridges, is the cutwater. This is a triangular extension at the bottom of a pier that guides water around, rather like the bow of a ship, to stop the river undermining the pier itself. These themselves are often built on wooden stakes, called starlings, driven into the riverbed. Often they are only on one side of the bridge – the upstream side. However on many, including the historic bridges over the Tamar, they are on both. And on many large arch bridges the cutwaters are built up to the level of the parapet, which makes a V-shaped diversion to incorporate it. These form refuges for pedestrians and Cornwall is particularly rich in bridges with this feature. An interesting variation is found on the Old Bridge at Marazion which has, possibly uniquely, semi-circular refuges.

Even today on bridges that have been widened but still lack a pavement, such as New Bridge at Gunnislake, they still form a welcome refuge for pedestrians from the traffic. However, on bridges that have been widened and generous pavements allowed, such as at Chapel Amble and Grampound, they look rather odd.

Not every arch bridge has refuges – for example, the lovely narrow bridge at Altarnun has none. By contrast, several railway viaducts have them, but extending out from the parapet, not the top of the piers.

The third type of bridge, the **cantilever**, consists of a beam supported at each end by brackets (rather than straight piers) so that the forces are dispersed in much the same way as on an arch bridge – downwards and outwards. One small example is the footbridge at Bodmin Parkway station, quite different from that at Redruth Station. The same principle is used on a large number of modern road viaducts, such as over the River Camel and the Dunheved Bridge.

Nanny Moore's Bridge at Bude and the disused swing bridge at Hayle are variants on the cantilever principle, where the beam can be supported at one end to create an opening. A modern variation is to support the beam not at the ends but along the edge, and this is how the extension to the Tamar Bridge was built – by hanging the new lanes off the sides of the existing deck.

The original Tamar Bridge was built as a **suspension bridge** – our fourth type. Here the deck is suspended by its edges from wires that connect to one of two thick cables. These cables loop over a tower at either end of the bridge and are anchored into solid ground at each end, so that the forces are mainly dispersed through these anchorages and towers. The Tamar Bridge's vital statistics are monumental. The deck weighs 8,000 tons and is suspended from two cables, each made of 31 cables $2^3/_8$ inches in diameter. These cables loop over the towers which stand 240ft above the decks before descending to the ground and into tunnels 50ft long.

The Royal Albert Bridge, just downstream of the Tamar Bridge, is also, in part a suspension bridge (or more precisely, two suspension bridges, end-to-end), but a very unusual rare one. Whereas the Tamar Bridge and all other 'proper' suspension bridges rely on anchorages in the ground to which to secure the cables, the Royal Albert's chains (which are used instead of cables) are attached to the ends of the

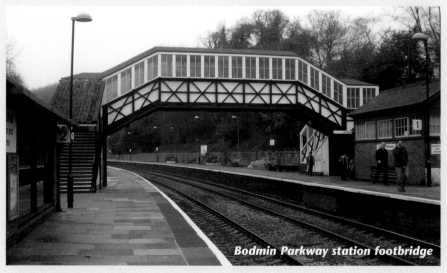
Bodmin Parkway station footbridge

tubular truss to create a closed system: the suspension bridge is in tension and the truss is in compression, so the two forces can be entirely contained within the structure.

The county's second oldest suspension bridge was built around 1902 to link Towan Island with the rest of Newquay. Although the island is now private, it has a history of teashops and in its early days a toll of 2d. was charged to cross the 100ft, long 4ft wide pedestrian bridge. It is said to be the only private suspension bridge in England.

The last (or first) bridge in England is also a suspension bridge for pedestrians, crossing Dollar Cove at Land's End to give a dramatic viewing point. The bridge itself is a rather utilitarian structure. The same cannot be said of the county's first bridge of the 21st century, the Halgavor suspension bridge. It has been designed so that as one drives along the A30 beneath it, the 'towers' – which in this case are stainless steel masts angled away from the bridge – are invisible and the bridge seems to float out of the trees. As a pedestrian, rider or cyclist about to use the bridge, the view is the complete opposite – the tops of the masts are seen through the trees long before the bridge itself comes into view.

Suspension was once the method for creating the world's longest bridges. However, today the longest bridges are built with a different technique: **cable staying**. Instead of the deck being supported by wires that run to cables looped over towers, the deck is supported by wires running from a single tower. However, cable stayed bridges do not have to be massive, and two examples in Cornwall are both modest. The Challenge Bridge in Wadebridge, a little upstream from the arch bridge, was built in 1991 and carries pedestrians over the Camel by means of a deck supported by sixteen wires fixed to a single tower. The Ross Bridge in Penzance, which opened ten years earlier, is a rather finer cable-stayed bridge but is also a swing bridge, opening to allow boats in and out of the dock.

The first bridge in England

Although the largest bridges (and the majority of those that are Scheduled Ancient Monuments), are concentrated in the east of the county, there are beautiful and interesting bridges scattered throughout Cornwall. This gazetteer highlights just a few as a starting point for exploring the county's bridge and viaduct heritage.

All the bridges that are Scheduled Ancient Monuments at the time of writing are included (**AM**). Where applicable the English Heritage Grade is also given (which is, in descending order of importance **G I**, **G II*** and **G II**). The two lists do not overlap entirely: few Ancient Monuments are also Listed Grade I. Furthermore, there are some notable structures that are neither Scheduled nor Listed, and the Listing is not necessarily a guide to the quality or beauty of a particular bridge. It should not be assumed that if a bridge is not included here it is of no interest – only a visit can establish this.

River bridges

River Neet and Bude Canal
Two fine bridges lie close to one another at **Helebridge** [SS 215 037], both Grade II. The earlier is a single round arch bridge over the Bude Canal, designed by James Green and opened in 1820. Almost alongside is a more elegant single segmental arch bridge with brick arch rings, built in 1839. In Bude, **Nanny Moore's Bridge** [SS 204 064] on The Strand is a Grade II three-span segmental arch bridge with an opening section on the westward end. Built in the 18th century or possibly earlier, it is thought to have been a cart and packhorse bridge.

The Tamar
The bridges of the Upper Tamar are unspectacular north of **Druxton Bridge** [SX 345 884]. There has been a bridge on this site since at least the 14th century. The

Higher New Bridge over the Tamar

present structure is a 16th century four-arch bridge, Grade II*. The western arch was rebuilt in the 19th century. **Higher New Bridge** [SX 348 866 – AM / G I] was the *pons novus juxta Launceston*, the construction of which was commissioned, with the help of revenue from the sale of Indulgences, by Bishop Oldham of Exeter in 1504 and was maintained by the Abbey of Tavistock. It is thought to have been built on top of an earlier structure – Nether Bridge – and is another example of the slightly pointed arch style, with three large arches and small floodwater arch. The cutwaters being carried up into the parapets to form refuges and within the western refuge on the upstream side is a late 18th century milestone, as the bridge formed part of the Launceston to Holsworthy turnpike road. The bridge was strengthened in the 20th century by inserting a concrete raft under the central arch – but fortunately without too much

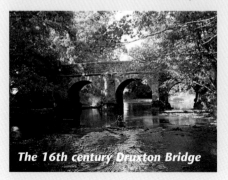

The 16th century Druxton Bridge

interference with the original design. However, its steeply curving approach roads made it increasingly unsuitable as part of a major road, and it is now by-passed by the modern Nether Bridge (opened in 1986) which carries the A388 over the Tamar.

Similarly, **Polson Bridge** [SX 355 849 – G II] was the principal crossing into Cornwall for hundreds of years until the building of the **Dunheved Bridge** in the 1970s. The current structure, a segmental arch bridge, was built in 1833 on the site of the old medieval bridge.

Further downstream, **Greystone Bridge** [SX 368 804 – AM / G I] is a four-arch bridge with round arches, and with two smaller arches on either side for floodwater. Built in 1439, it is very probably the work of the same architect as **Horsebridge** [SX 400 748 – AM / GII], 14 miles below. Built two years earlier than Greystone, it has five round arches each with a span of 18ft , with one smaller arch at each end, and is around 72ft in total length. Curiously for a round arch bridge, the floodwater arch at the western end is pointed. It has refuges on both sides and below those on the northern side corbel-like projections, hollowed underneath, and thought to hold the wooden posts of a salmon hatch. The bridge has been widened by 2ft on the downstream side but, set on a quiet road between Stoke Climsland and Tavistock, it is particularly picturesque.

New Bridge at Gunnislake [SX 433 722 – AM], also known as Gunnislake Bridge, was built in the early 16th century with six slightly pointed arches of white granite. Widened in 1809, it is still inadequate for two lanes of traffic, but all the cutwaters are built up to create refuges on both sides of the bridge.

For a short time after its opening in 1961, the **Tamar Bridge** [SX 435 588] was the longest suspension bridge in the UK. Before its completion, Plymouth was linked to Saltash only by ferry and the Royal Albert railway bridge. To cope with increasing traffic, it was extended in 2002 by cantilevering additional lanes off the sides.

River Ottery

The oldest datable bridge in Cornwall, **Yeolm Bridge** [SX 318 873 – AM /GI], dates from about 1300. It is a text book example of the ribbed vault method of construction in bridge building and bears a very close resemblance to the North Gate of Launceston Castle. The bridge has two pointed arches, each with three ribs, and a floodwater arch on the southern side. Unfortunately it was widened thoughtlessly on the east side, but the west side is more or less completely unaltered.

River Kensey

The Packhorse Bridge in Launceston [SX 327 850 – AM / GI] is a curious five-arch bridge is thought to date from the 15th century, with some later modifications. The arches are of three styles – the central one is almost semi-circular, those on either side are slightly pointed and the outermost are segmental. It lies very low in the water and has no parapet, but railings were added in the 19th century. In the 18th century, traffic was taken off this bridge by the nearby

The 15th century Greystone Bridge

St Thomas's Bridge (with which it is sometimes confused) which carries the A388 though the town, which has left the packhorse bridge in an idyllic setting. St Thomas's Bridge has two arches over the Kensey and an additional arch over a leat for a now-disused mill. A Grade II structure, it was at one time a Scheduled Ancient Monument itself (perhaps as a result of confusing it with the packhorse bridge), but it is spoilt by both the volume of traffic and a large pipe laid across the upstream side.

The graceful Trekelland Bridge

River Inny and tributaries

Polyphant Bridge [SX 266 823 – AM / G II] is a two-arch bridge, the eastern span of which probably dates from the 17th century. The Western arch was rebuilt after the 1847 flood. It once carried the main road from Launceston to Bodmin, before the road was diverted through Two Bridges in the early 19th century. It is marked on the Ordnance Survey maps as Hick's Mill. A G II mid-19th century three-span bridge lies to the south [SX 259 815].

Altarnun Bridge [SX 223 812 – AM / G II] is earlier than Polyphant, being built somewhere between the late 15th and early 17th centuries. This two-span bridge was widened unsympathetically in the early 20th century with iron girders.

The remote but beautiful Trekenner Bridge

However, when later in the century a new bridge was built a few yards away, the bridge was restored to its original width. The cutwaters are built up, but only to the level of the arches – they do not form refuges. It is now used only by pedestrians, and, set close to the church, creates a chocolate box vista. Further down the Inny, a three-span, semi-circular arch bridge over Pen Pont Water, **Trerithick Bridge** [SX 244 819 – AM / GII] was rebuilt in the 19th century to accommodate the turnpike road, but is now on a quiet backroad. Unfortunately, it is difficult to see the bridge properly from the road, and access to the River Inny is very difficult. Much more accessible is **Trekelland Bridge** [SX 300 798 – AM / G II*] on the B3254. Built around 1520, it has two large and one small pointed arches and is considered one of the best preserved and most graceful of bridges in the county.

In remoteness, however, **Trekenner Bridge** [SX 339 770 – G II] excels, but is worth seeking out. The bridge ceased to be of importance when the Launceston to Callington turnpike diverted the route through Woodabridge. This very lovely three-arch bridge probably dates back to the 16th century. **Trecarrell Bridge** [SX 321 773 – GII], where Charles I crossed with his army in August 1644, was swept away in the 1847 flood, and was replaced by the current single span segmental arch bridge.

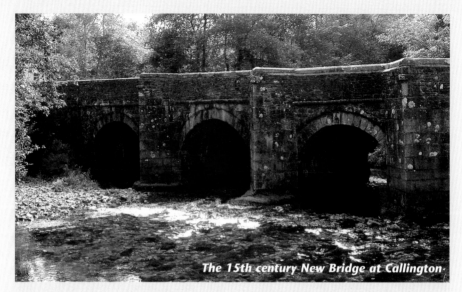

The 15th century New Bridge at Callington

River Lynher

The three-arch **Beriow Bridge** [SX 273 756 – AM / G II*] was built in the mid-16th century but was sensitively widened in 1890, using the same design and materials. The arches are round and the cutwaters are extended to form two refuges in each parapet. Equally interesting is a rare survival of a beam bridge from the medieval period, further downstream, **Starabridge** [SX 289 738 – AM] is a substantial three-span beam bridge leading to Rillaton, which in medieval times was an important administrative centre. With the decline of Rillaton, the bridge was superceded by the one at Rilla Mill (where the present structure dates from the 1890s). It has a later flood channel on the eastern side.

The **New Bridge at Callington** [SX 347 679 – AM / GII*] is also medieval and first recorded in 1478. However, it is a four-arch bridge. Rebuilt in 1698 and widened in 1874 on the south side, it has corbels on the cutwaters similar to those on Horse Bridge on the Tamar. The arches are semi-circular. Nearby, in a particularly lovely location stands **Clapper Bridge** [SX 351 652 – AM / G II]. Its name suggests that it was once a stone beam bridge, but it is now a three semi-circular arch bridge,

dating from the late 17th or 18th centuries, with two refuges on its upstream side. To the northeast [SX 359 664] there is a 19th century Grade II arch bridge rebuilt in the early 20th.

River Fowey and tributaries

Crossing the Warleggan is **Temple Old Bridge** [SX 150 737 – AM], now by-passed by the A30. This single arch bridge is not itself at all spectacular, but its location on the old turnpike road again warrants a diversion. A much more impressive structure, over the Fowey, is the three-arch **Treverbyn Old Bridge** [SX 206 674 – AM / G II*]. It was built in 1412-13, when an indulgence was granted by Bishop Stafford of Exeter, but its western arch is probably part of an even earlier

Treverbyn Old Bridge over the Fowey

Panter's Bridge across the Warleggan

structure. Widened in the 18th century, it was by-passed by a new bridge in 1929 built alongside, leaving it intact. **Panter's Bridge** [SX 158 680 – AM / G II*], again across the Warleggan, is similarly redundant thanks to a new bridge alongside. This was once on the main route from Liskeard to Bodmin, but became a by-way with the building of a new turnpike road (now the A38). The bridge is a two-arch structure, the arches being slightly pointed. It was built in the early 15th century and incorporates part of an earlier bridge in the southwest abutment.

Respryn was once one of the most important strategic points in Cornwall and there has been a bridge here since at least 1300. The current **Respryn Bridge** [SX 099 634 – AM / G II*] dates from the 15th

A postcard view of the refuges on Respryn Bridge

A romantic view of Lostwithiel Bridge

century, but its two western-most arches have been rebuilt. The other three are original. The four cutwaters on the upstream side are extended to form refuges, but there are only two refuges on the downstream side. Close to Lanhydrock House, and with very little traffic crossing, it is one of the most picturesque of Cornwall's bridges.

Lostwithiel Bridge [SX 106 598 – AM / G II], by contrast, is in the very heart of a bustling town. It is believed to date from an Indulgence of 1437 granted by Bishop Lacy, but it is almost certainly built on the site of an earlier crossing. It has five original pointed arches to which have been added a number of flood arches. An earlier inspector of Ancient Monuments noted ominously that 'there is constant agitation for its removal'. Like Respryn Bridge, the bridge saw considerable action in the Civil War. Built a little later, at the head of a small creek which flows down to the Fowey estuary, stands the pretty **Lerryn Bridge** [SX 140 571 – AM / G II*]. It dates from around 1500 and in 1573 Queen Elizabeth issued an order to the bailiff and constables of the Hundred of the West to levy a rate for the erecting and re-edifying of a decayed bridge called 'Laryon Bridge'. Originally the bridge had three pointed arches, but one has been filled. Also in the village is Lower Town Bridge (G II), south west of Red Store, is a mid- to late-19th century single arch bridge.

The Lower Town Bridge at Lerryn, as it once was

A stone beam bridge at Bradford

River Camel

The upper reaches of the Camel and its tributaries are crossed by numerous beam bridges. Some fine examples are on the De Lank river – such as **Bradford Bridge** [SX 119 754 – G II], a four-span bridge built in the 17th century and widened in the mid-20th, with a Grade II single span footbridge nearby; the five-span **Delford Bridge** [SX 114 759 – G II], a 19th century five-span bridge and the seven-span **Gam Bridge** [SX 088 778 – GII], the latter two both built after the 1847 flood swept away earlier structures.

Delford Bridge over the De Lank

The sundial post on Keybridge

The last bridge on the De Lank before it joins the Camel is **Keybridge** [SX 089 739 – G II]. Built in the early 17th century, or possibly earlier, it has one round arch and one pointed arch. Uniquely in Cornwall, it has a post for a sundial in a refuge. A bridge is known to have existed at Helland in 1381 but the current **Helland Bridge** [SX 065 715 – AM / G II*] dates from the early 15th century and was described in the 16th century by John Leyland as 'the first memorable bridge on the Alainie'. This fine four-arch bridge, complete with refuges, is rather like a small version of the Lostwithiel Bridge. The granite lintel on the west wall is possibly from the rebuilding after the 1847 flood. **Ruthernbridge** [SX 012 668 – AM / G II*], on a small tributary to the west, again resembles Lostwithiel Bridge but on an even smaller scale. This two-arch bridge dating from around 1530 has not been widened.

The bridge at **Wadebridge** [SW 991 724 – AM / G II*], on the other hand, was the largest bridge in Cornwall from 1470 to 1859. It has been repaired and widened so many times – in 1874, 1952 and 1963 – that it is an education in itself in the history of arch bridge construction. Although two of its fifteen arches are now blocked, it is still the structurally most impressive bridge

The 15th century Helland Bridge

The 16th century Ruthernbridge

The cable-stayed Challenge Bridge at Wadebridge

of them all. Close by is the modern cable-stayed **Challenge Bridge** [SW 994 722]. **Trewornan Bridge** [SW 987 743 – AM / G II], on the River Amble, has the appearance of a medieval bridge, complete with pointed arches and refuges, but not the history. It was built in 1791, at the instigation of the local vicar. The parapets were partly rebuilt in the late 20th century.

Wadebridge at the beginning of the 20th century

The Fal and tributaries

One of the oldest bridge crossings in this area is **Tregony Bridge** [SW 922 448 – G II], where there has been a crossing since at least 1382. The current structure, however, a single span, segmental arch bridge, was built in 1893. The single richest village for bridges is Perranarworthal, the location of the **Perran Iron Works' iron bridge** [SW 775 384 – AM / G II]. This is a beam bridge with balustraded parapets of cast iron in a gothic style. The foundry itself, which cast the bridge, was established in 1791 and became one of the most important in the county. The bridge originally linked the foundry with the works office, but was moved a few yards in the 20th century when alterations were made to the works. At the time of writing, the bridge is inaccessible as the whole site awaits redevelopment. Elsewhere in the village are an early/mid- 19th century single span segmental arch bridge [SW 777 385]; a single span arch bridge on Truro-Falmouth turnpike road originally built in 1828 [SW 778 387]; and an early 5 span beam bridge of the early 19th century on the former main road [SW 786 400].

Helston

Bridging the Polwheveral stream which flows into the creek of the same name and then into the Helston river the single span **Polwheveral Bridge** [SW 738 285 – G II*] was built in 1572 and widened in the 19th century. Its interest lies not only in the fact that the contract for its construction survives, as we have seen, but also because, while the 16th century bridge is of vaulted arch construction, the 19th century widening was accomplished by laying granite blocks alongside. Thus it is both an arch and a beam bridge.

The oldest arch bridge in the west: St Erth

A hidden railway relic at Hayle

The gatehouse on a bridge at 'Foxstones'

Hayle

The town of Hayle has several interesting bridges, including two Scheduled Ancient Monuments. **Black Bridge** [SW 566 381 – AM, G II], or Sea Lane Bridge, is a two-span segmental arch bridge built in 1818 of scoria blocks. The two arches are of neither the same height nor width. Nearby is the **Old Railway Bridge** [SW 567 382 – AM] of 1837, which formed part of the Hayle Railway. It now merges so well with the footpath that it is difficult to spot. The town also has a now-disused swing bridge for the former railway and road to cross the canal, built in 1880.

The West

Marazion Old Bridge [SW 513 312 – G II] is a rare unaltered 18th century road bridge with semi-circular (in contrast to the usual triangular) refuges. It has survived thanks to the building of **Marazion Bridge** [SW 513 311 – G II], an unusually wide single span arch bridge, in 1837 as part of a turnpike. There appear to be no other large bridges of great age in the west of the county, although **St Erth Bridge** [SW 549 351 – G II] is a 19th century three-span arch bridge, a rebuilding of the 1633 bridge, itself on the site of a medieval bridge.

However, for an interesting collection of smaller bridges, **Penberth Cove** [SW 399 230 – 403 227] is well worth visiting. Its beam bridges include an unaltered 17th century three-span footbridge, an unsurfaced 18th century two-span bridge and, outside the private residence "Foxstones", a gatehouse built on a bridge.

Railway viaducts

There are 41 viaducts on the railway lines from Plymouth to Falmouth and Penzance, all of which are replacements for the earlier viaducts designed by I.K. Brunel. They cross some of the most beautiful valleys in Cornwall, and these lofty structures have an imposing beauty of their own. Those that have been listed by English Heritage are, from east to west:

Forder Viaduct [SX 414 576 – G II], also known as Anthony Passage, 606 ft long, maximum height 67 ft, eight arches, built in 1906.

Nottar Viaduct [SX 378 578 – G II]. 921 ft long, 67ft high, eight arches, built in 1908, 300 yards downstream of the original viaduct.

St Germans Viaduct [SX 365 575 – G II], 945ft, 106ft high, thirteen arches, built in 1908.

Moorswater Viaduct [SX 236 640 – G II*], 954ft long, 147ft high, eight arches, built in 1881. The piers of the earlier viaduct remain. The only viaduct graded II*.

St Pinnock Viaduct [SX 177 646 – G II], 633ft long. The piers of Brunel's 1856 viaduct were heightened in 1882 to 151ft making this the tallest viaduct in the county.

East Largin Viaduct [SX 172 646 – G II], 567ft long, 130ft high, eight piers built in 1885-6 and extended and the wooden structure replaced with iron girders in 1886.

West Largin Viaduct [SX 166 648 – G II], 315ft long, 75ft high, three arches, built in 1875 the first of the masonry arch viaducts built to replace Brunel's wooden structures.

St Germans Viaduct Alan Kittridge

Redruth Viaduct MICHAEL MESSENGER

Derrycombe Viaduct [SX 156 651 – G II], 369ft long, 77ft high, four piers, built in 1881. The piers from the 1857 viaduct stand alongside.

Clinnick Viaduct [SX 146 652 – G II], 330ft long, 74ft high, six arches, built in 1879 alongside the earlier structure.

Penadlake Viaduct [SX 135 650 – G II], 42ft long, 42ft high, eight arches, built in 1877.

Gover Viaduct [SW 999 53 – G II], 690 ft long, 95 ft high, 8 arches, built in 1898 on the north side of the earlier viaduct, the piers of which remain.

Coombe St Stephens Viaduct [SW 944 511 – G II], 738ft, 70ft high, 10 arches, built in 1898.

Fal Viaduct [SW 937 507 – G II], 570ft long, 90ft high, 7 arches, built in 1884.

Truro Viaduct [SW 825 453 – G II], also known as the Moresk Viaduct. At 1,329ft it is the longest in Cornwall, 92ft high, 18 arches, built in 1904. Fifteen of Brunel's original piers stand alongside.

Carvedras Viaduct [SW 816 450 – G II], 969ft long, 86ft high,11 arches, built in 1904. Five piers from the original viaduct stand alongside.

On the Truro–Falmouth line:

Collegewood Viaduct [SW 781 342 – G II], 954ft long, 100ft high, 11 arches, built in 1934 to replace the last of the wooden viaducts in Cornwall

On the Truro–Penzance line:

Penwethers Viaduct [SW 799 440 – G II] 372ft long, 54ft high, seven arches, built in 1887.

Redruth Viaduct [SW 698 418 – G II], 489ft long, 61ft high, 8 arches, built in 1888.

Angarrack Viaduct [SW 584 381 – G II]. 798ft long, 100ft high, 11 arches, built in 1885.

45

Calstock Viaduct ALAN KITTRIDGE

Other viaducts of note

Calstock Viaduct [SX 434 687– G II*], 12-span viaduct, built of concrete blocks and completed in 1908.

Treffry Viaduct [SX 056 571– AM], 600ft long, 90ft high, ten arches, built 1839–1842 by Joseph Treffry for a horse-drawn railway.

Trenance Viaduct [SW 8061-8161– G II], seven arches, built in 1874 to replace a timber viaduct carrying a branch line into Newquay over the Trenance Valley.

Lappa Viaduct [SW 837 581 – G II], built in 1840 by Joseph Treffry to carry his tramway from East Wheal Rose mine to Newquay (now dismantled) over the River Lappa. Altered in perhaps 1905.

Other railway bridges of note

Royal Albert Bridge at Saltash [SX 435 587], the greatest bridge of the Victorian era: a two-span suspension and trussed beam bridge in one, designed by I. K. Brunel, opened in 1859 and still in use today.

Carylon Bay [SW 055 523], a railway bridge build in 1859 in a gothic style.

Portreath Incline [SW 657 452 – G II] A bridge beneath a railway incline built in 1837, by the Hayle Railway. The incline forms the final descent from the Carn Brea mining area to Portreath Harbour.

Wainsford [SX 151 651 – G II]. An accommodation bridge to link two fields. Built 1859, it is a splendid example of the quality to which the Cornwall Railway constructed, even for the most modest of access routes. There is also a pretty (unlisted) arch road bridge over the Fowey to the north of the hamlet.

Footbridge at Redruth station [SW 700 420 – G II). A largely unaltered example of a railway footbridge of 1888, decorated in the Egyptian style.

Bridge at Hill Head, Penryn [SW 786 340], a fine example of a parabolic arch bridge built in 1863, under the Falmouth branch: a little known Brunel design.

The Royal Albert Bridge, Saltash

The packhorse bridge at Porthcothan

Other significant bridges mentioned in the text

Chyverton House [SW 798 512 – G II*], unaltered single arch bridge of c. 1780 in landscaped garden.

East Looe Bridge [SX 255 536 – G II], a seven-span segmental arch bridge, erected in 1853 replacing a medieval one.

Halgavor Bridge [SX 085 646], hi-tech suspension bridge over the A30 to carry a bridle- and cycle way.

Haunch Bridge [SX 327 916 – G II], single arch accommodation bridge built over the Bude Canal in 1823.

Lanner: bridge at Rough Street [SW 712 395 – G II], built in 1838 for the now-dismantled Hayle Railway.

Morwenstow: King William's Bridge [SS 216 147 – G II], a single span segmental arch bridge, 1836.

Polperro: Roman Bridge [SX 208 508 – G II], a single arch bridge of unknown date but certainly not Roman. The town also has "Saxon Bridge", a beam bridge built in the 1860s and Mill Bridge (Mill Hill), an arch bridge again built in the 1860s.

Porthcothan Mill [SW 862 718], a completely unaltered packhorse bridge with a medieval appearance, which, surprisingly, has not been listed.

Roughtor Farm [SX 139 818 – G II], an unsurfaced beam bridge in an unparalleled setting in the heart of Bodmin Moor.

Slaughterbridge [SX 109 855 – G II], an 18th century three-span beam bridge.

Two Bridges [SX 271 817 – G II], an 18th century arch bridge, now bypassed by a widened A30.

A simple beam bridge at Roughtor

The 18th century Slaughterbridge

Narrowed and then bypassed: Trevemper Bridge near Newquay

GLOSSARY

Abutment: the end support of an arch bridge.

Accommodation bridge: a bridge cut through an embankment, usually for access to farmers' fields.

Coping: the top band of stones on a parapet.

Cutwater: a triangular-shaped extension of a pier to cleave the water and thus lessen the scouring of the base of the **pier** by the water.

Deck: that part of the bridge that forms the roadway or footway.

Parapet: a wall along the side of the bridge.

Pier: the support between two spans of a bridge.

Refuge: a recess in the parapet to shelter pedestrians from traffic..

Skew bridge: a bridge built not square but at an angle to the road or waterway it crosses.

Soffit: the underside of the **deck** (or any other surface).

Viaduct: a bridge carrying a road or railway across a valley.

Voussoir: a wedge shaped brick or stone used in the construction of arches.